st

stamp

__ar

__airs

__op

__ool

__ep

put a stamp on the envelope.

_____ can be seen in the sky at
ght.

red traffic light tells a driver
_____ .

/e go up the _____ to bed.

he milk is on the _____ by the door.

sat on the _____ .

th

__umb

__imble

__in

__ief

__istle

__orns

The _____ stole the lady's bag.

The _____ is a prickly plant.

My dad wears a _____ on his finger when he sews.

I am not fat. I am _____ .

A rose bush has _____ on it.

I have four fingers and a _____ on each hand.

sp

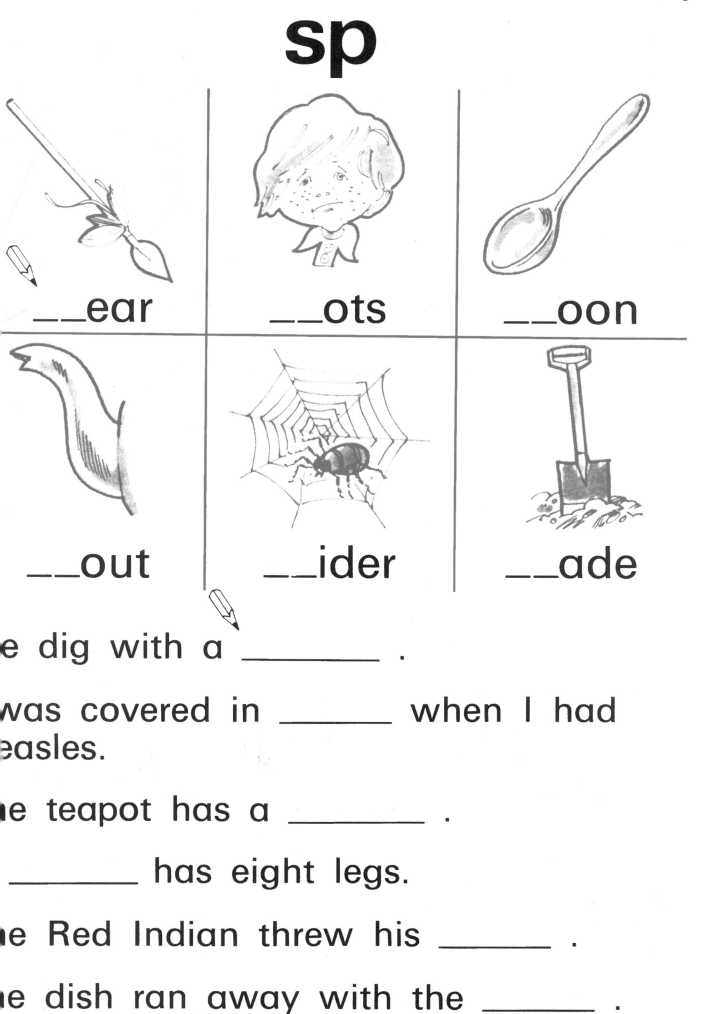

__ear   __ots   __oon

__out   __ider   __ade

e dig with a _____ .

was covered in _____ when I had
easles.

e teapot has a _____ .

_____ has eight legs.

e Red Indian threw his _____ .

e dish ran away with the _____ .

sm

__ell

__ile

__all

__ash

__oke

__ock

A mouse is a _____ animal.

_____ comes out of a chimney.

We _____ when we are happy.

I can _____ with my nose.

A glass could _____ if you dropped

I wear a _____ to keep paint off my clothes.

sk

__i

__ip

__y

__ittles

__irt

__ate

use a rope to _____ .

can _____ on the ice.

like to _____ in the snow.

ane is wearing a new _____ .

/e play _____ with daddy.

here is an aeroplane in the _____ .

sc

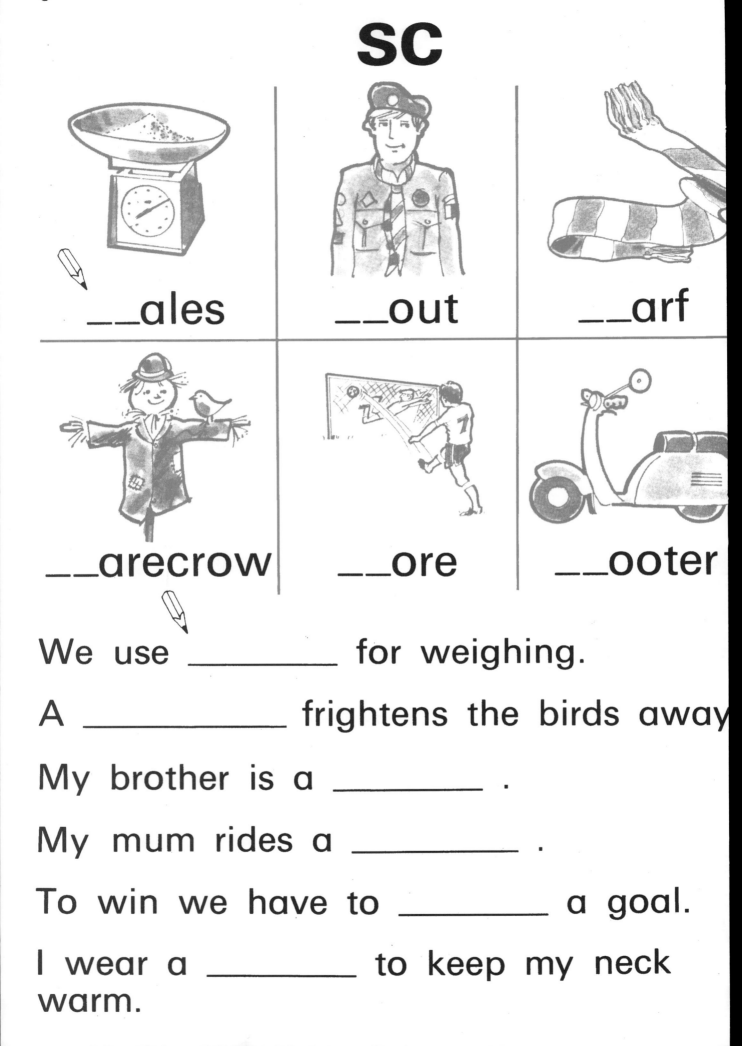

__ales

__out

__arf

__arecrow

__ore

__ooter

We use _____ for weighing.

A _____ frightens the birds away

My brother is a _____ .

My mum rides a _____ .

To win we have to _____ a goal.

I wear a _____ to keep my neck warm.

sn

__owman   __ake   __out

__owdrop   __ail   __ap

like playing _____ with my cards.

_____ has his house on his back.

_____ is a flower.

pig has a _____ .

Ve made a big _____ with the snow.

he _____ slides through the grass.

SW

__eater

__ing

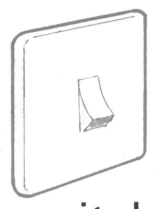

__itch

__eets

__im

__an

I like eating _____

I wear a _____ when I am cold.

It is fun to play on the _____ in the park.

I _____ on the light.

We _____ in the sea.

The _____ swims in the river.

sm   th   sp   sk

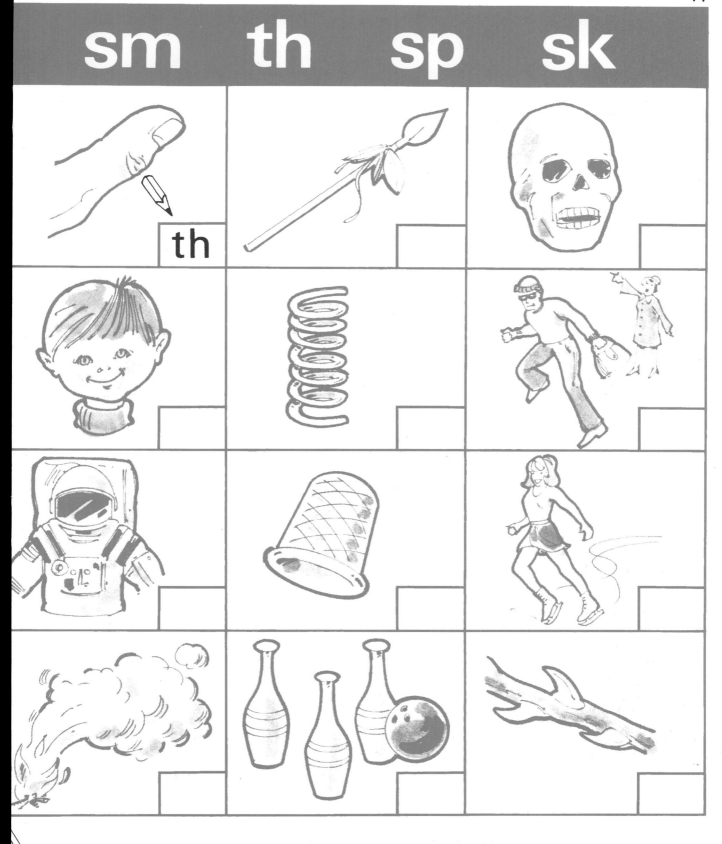

th

thumb   __ief   __ittles   __oke

__aceman   __ull   __ile   __ear

__ater   __orns   __imble   __iral

sc sw st sn

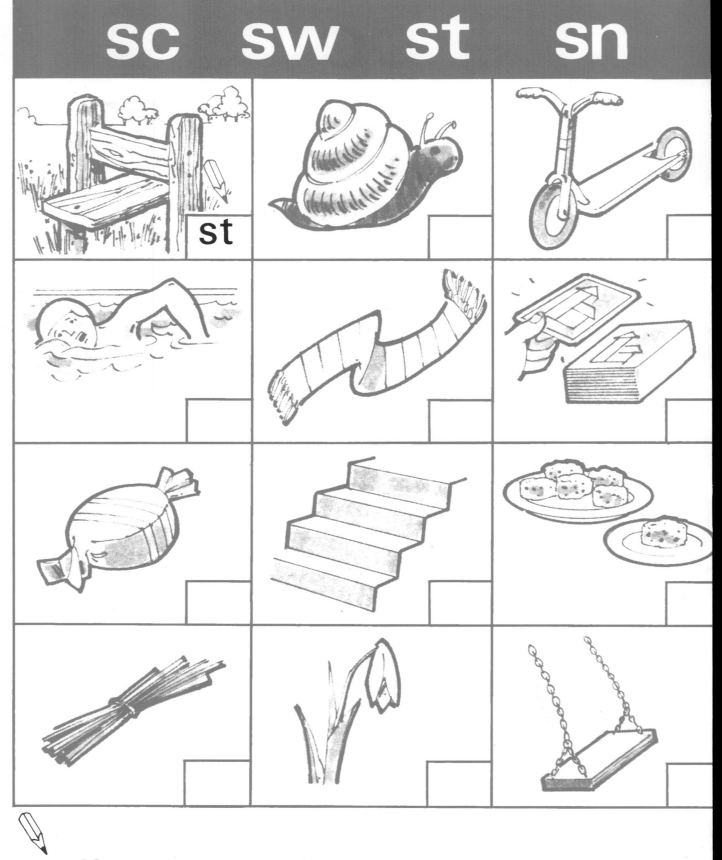

st

stile   __owdrop   __one   __ap

__ing   __arf   __immer   __oote

__icks   __eet   __ail   __eps

OO

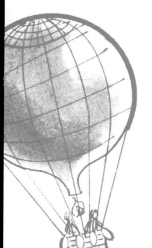

balloon

balloon

b__t

z__

st__l

sch__l

f__d

m__n

_ _ _ _ _

_ _ _

_ _ _ _

_ _ _ _ _ _

_ _ _ _

ee

f__t   sh__p   wh__l

tr__   b__   sl__p

The _____ flies from flower to flower.

A wheelbarrow often has only
one _____ .

John can climb up this _____ in the
garden.

I have two hands and two _____ .

I go to _____ in bed.

We get wool from _____ .

ea

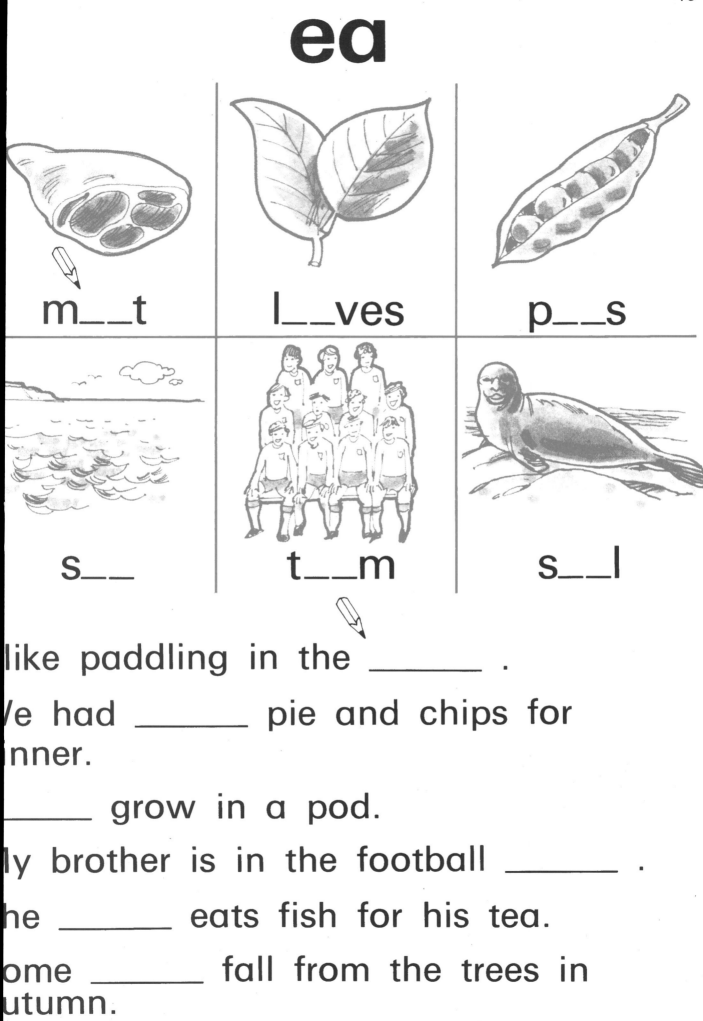

m___t   l__ves   p__s

s__   t__m   s__l

like paddling in the _____ .

Ve had _____ pie and chips for
inner.

_____ grow in a pod.

ly brother is in the football _____ .

he _____ eats fish for his tea.

ome _____ fall from the trees in
utumn.

oa

c___ch	r__d	t__d	c__t

b__t	f__l	m__t

I wear a _____ in winter.

I saw a _____ sailing in the water.

A baby horse is called a _____ .

Some castles have a _____ around them.

The _____ was going down the _____

A _____ was sitting by the pond.

ou

m__ntain

m__se

cl__ds

m__th

h__se

r__ndab__t

_____ likes cheese.

Open your _____ wide," the dentist says.

We go on a _____ at the fair.

There are _____ in the sky when it rains.

I live in a _____ .

There was snow on top of the _____ .

ai

sn__l   n__l   s__l   tr__n

r__ls   r__n   t__l

The dog is wagging his _____ .

The _____ has a shell on its back.

The boat has a large _____ .

I hit the _____ with my hammer.

I got wet in the _____ .

The _____ runs along the _____ .

ay

pl__

h__

tr__

d__

pr__

cr__ons

ows eat _____ in winter.

_____ games with my friends.

colour pictures with my _____ .

ome people go to church to _____ .

he sun is out during the _____ .

lummy uses a _____ for carrying cups.

aw

___

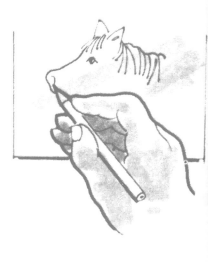

_____

_ _ _ _ _ _

s__

p__

cl__

dr__

cr__l

sh__l

dr__er

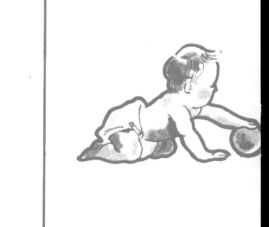

_____

___

_____

_ _ _ _ _ _

ar

sh__k

p__cel

p__k

c__

f__m

c__t

c__d

____

_____

____

_____

_____

____

____

or

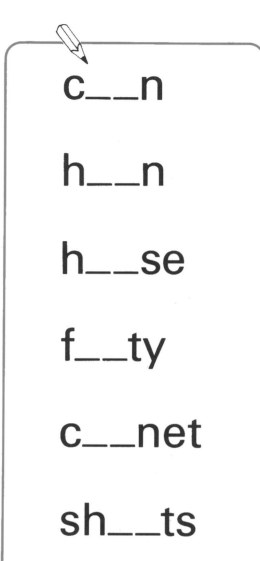

c__n

h__n

h__se

f__ty

c__net

sh__ts

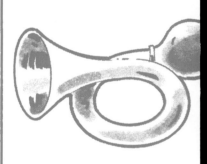

_____

_____

_____

____

40

_____   _____

OW

__l

c___

t__el

t__er

fl__er

cl__n

cr__n

_____

_____

_____

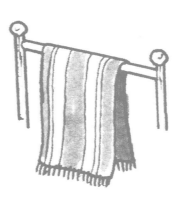

____

_____

_____

oo oa or ee ea

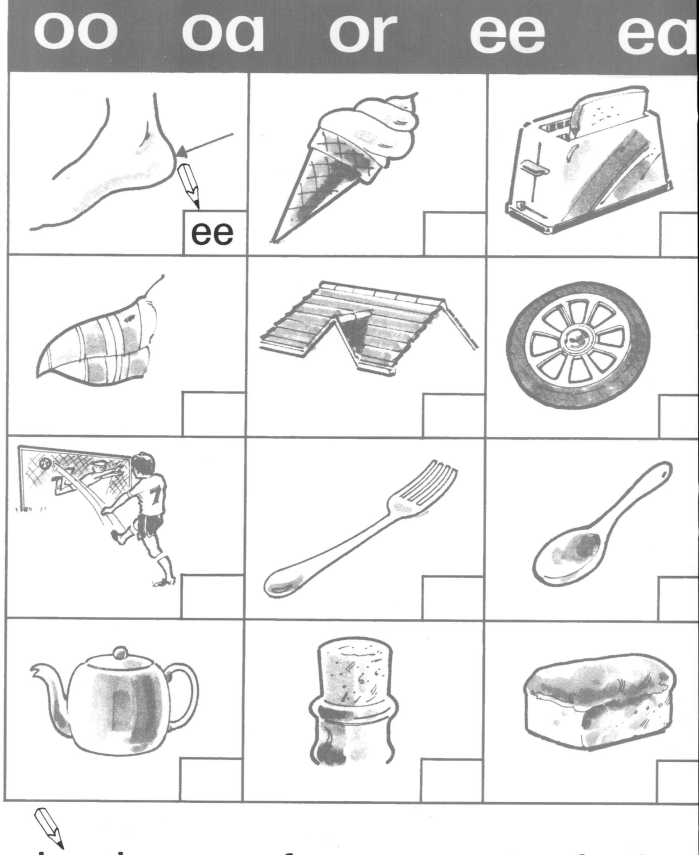

ee

h__l   r__f   sp__n   f__k

g__l   t__ster   c__k   ice-cr__n

wh__l   l__f   t__pot   b__k

ay ai ar aw ow ou

ay

M___   st___   ch__n   __l

cl___   tr___   __m   p__nt

h___se   t__el   m__se   y__n

-st

fir__

cru__

gho__

ne__

toa__

ve__

A bird lays eggs in a _____ .

My dog won _____ prize.

Some children wear a _____ to keep them warm.

A loaf of bread has a _____ .

Mummy makes _____ for breakfast.

A _____ can scare people.

27

-er

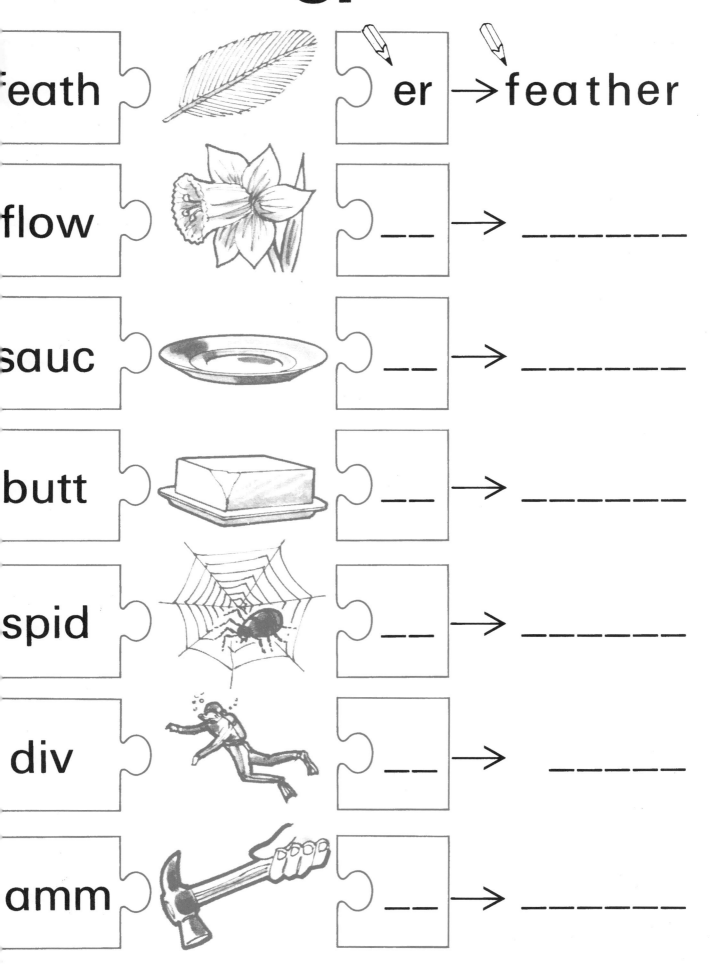

feath | er → feather

flow | __ → _____

sauc | __ → _____

butt | __ → _____

spid | __ → _____

div | __ → _____

amm | __ → _____

e

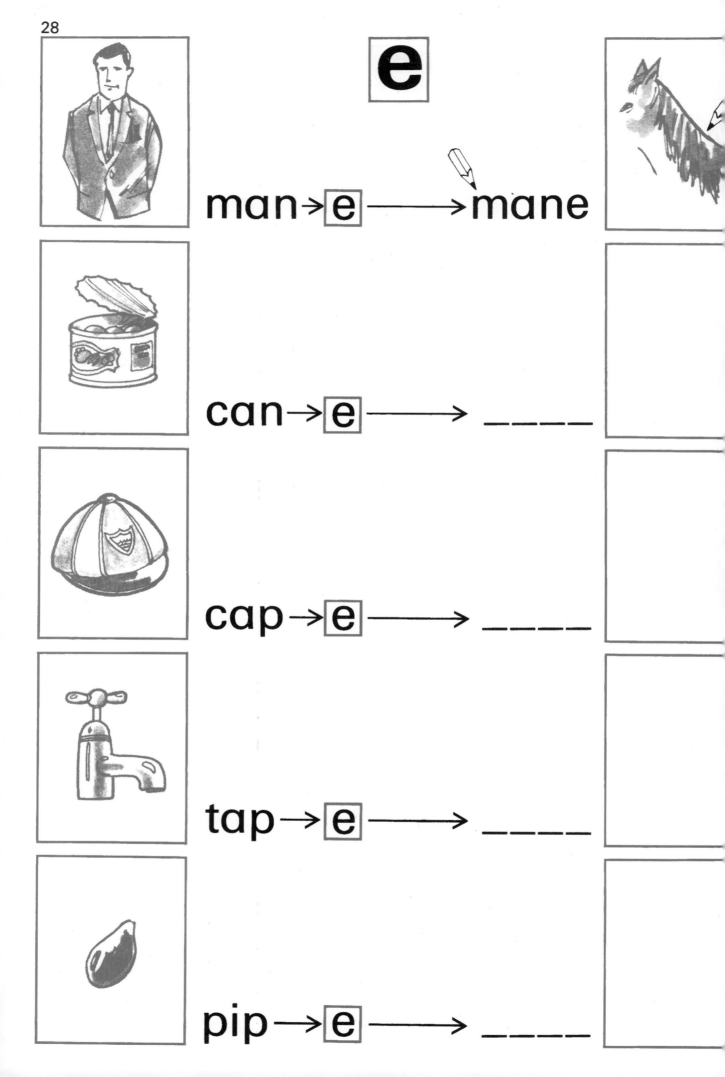

man → e ⟶ mane

can → e ⟶ _____

cap → e ⟶ _____

tap → e ⟶ _____

pip → e ⟶ _____

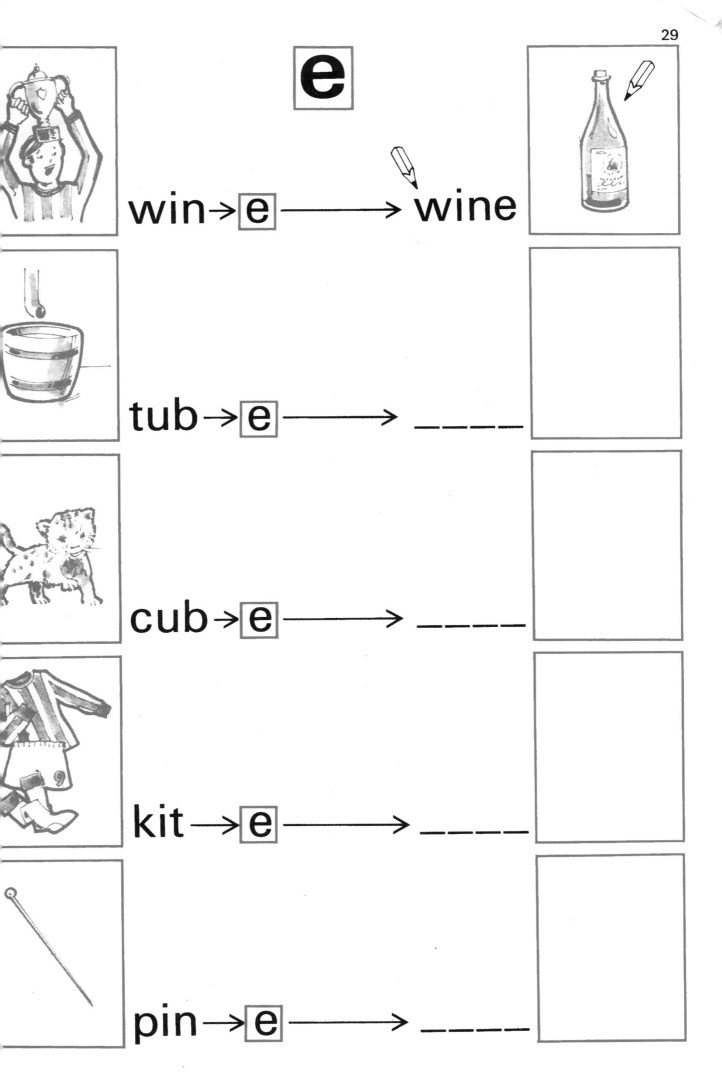

e

win → e ⟶ wine

tub → e ⟶ _____

cub → e ⟶ _____

kit → e ⟶ _____

pin → e ⟶ _____

30

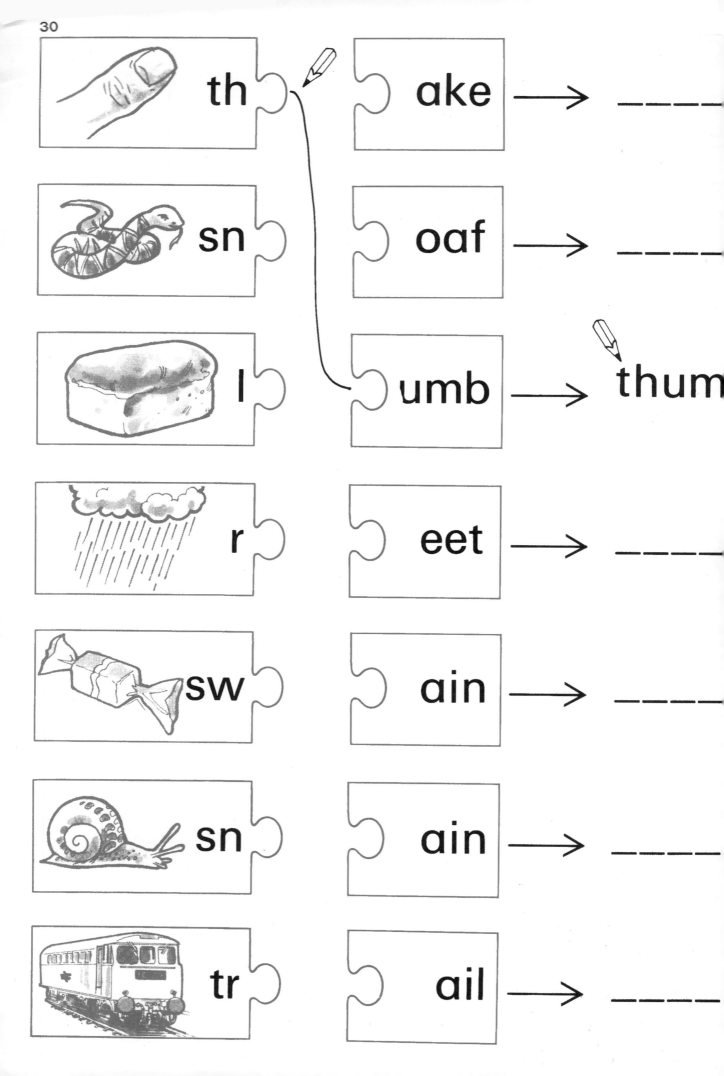

th

sn

l

r

sw

sn

tr

ake

oaf

umb → thum

eet

ain

ain

ail

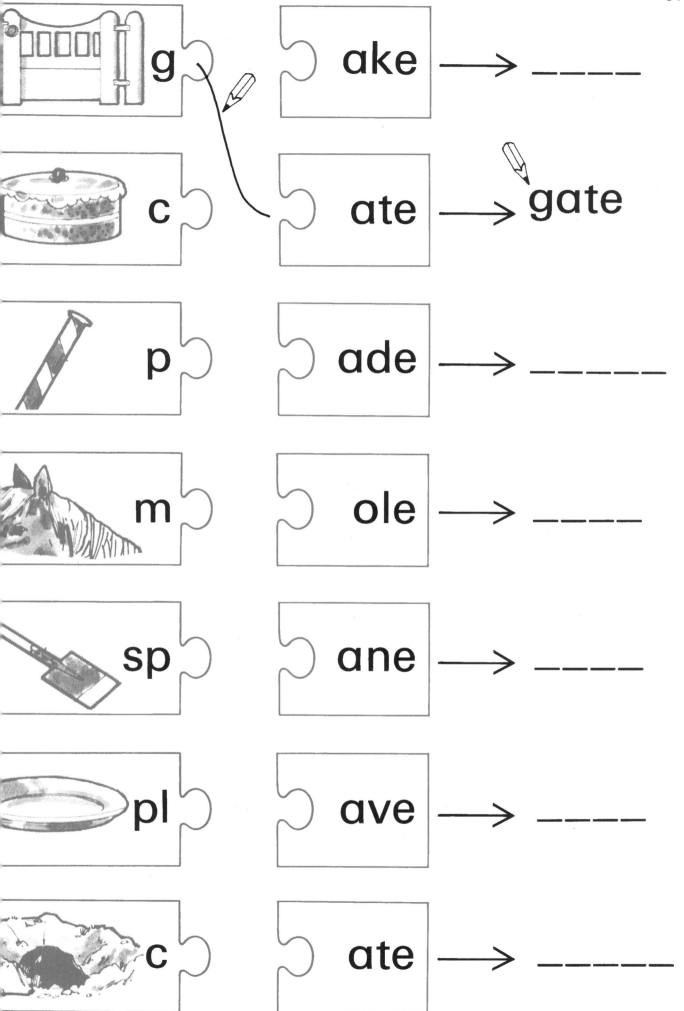

g | ake → _ _ _ _

c | ate → gate

p | ade → _ _ _ _ _

m | ole → _ _ _ _

sp | ane → _ _ _ _

pl | ave → _ _ _ _

c | ate → _ _ _ _ _ _

Schofield & Sims

the long-established educational publisher
specialising in maths, English and science materials for schools

Sound Practice is a series of graded activity books that help children to learn the sound and spelling patterns necessary for reading and writing.

Sound Practice Book 5 includes:

- Consonant blends (for example, 'sc' and 'sp')
- Single sounds made by more than one letter (for example, 'th', 'ow' and 'ai')
- Breaking words into beginnings and endings (onset and rime)
- 'Magic e' at the end of a word.

This book is suitable for children in Key Stage 1.

The full range of titles in the series is as follows:

Sound Practice Book 1:   ISBN 978 07217 0862 1

Sound Practice Book 2:   ISBN 978 07217 0863 8

Sound Practice Book 3:   ISBN 978 07217 0864 5

Sound Practice Book 4:   ISBN 978 07217 0865 2

Sound Practice Book 5:   ISBN 978 07217 0866 9

Have you tried **First Phonics** by Schofield & Sims?
This is a series of graded activity books that help children to learn the sounds, spelling patterns and word-building skills necessary for reading and writing.

**For further information and to place your order
visit www.schofieldandsims.co.uk or telephone 01484 607080**

ISBN 978 07217 0866 9

**£2.45
(Retail price)**

Key Stage 1
Age range: 5–7 years

(This is a practice series, so some
of the contents overlap with the
Early Years Foundation Stage)

Schofield & Sims

Dogley Mill, Fenay Bridge, Huddersfield HD8 0NQ
Phone: 01484 607080 Facsimile: 01484 606815
E-mail: sales@schofieldandsims.co.uk
www.schofieldandsims.co.uk

ISBN 978-07217-0866-9

9 780721 708669